Showstoppers

Wise Publications
London/New York/Paris/Sydney/
Copenhagen/Madrid

Exclusive Distributors:
Music Sales Limited
8/9 Frith Street, London W1V 5TZ, England.
Music Sales Pty Limited
120 Rothschild Avenue, Rosebery, NSW 2018, Australia.

Order No. AM959080
ISBN 0-7119-7939-1
This book © Copyright 1999 by Wise Publications

Music compiled and arranged by Stephen Duro
Music processed by Allegro Reproductions
Cover photograph courtesy of Rex Features

Printed in the United Kingdom by
Halstan & Co Limited, Amersham, Buckinghamshire.

Your Guarantee of Quality
As publishers, we strive to produce every book to the highest commercial standards.
The music has been freshly engraved and the book has been carefully designed to minimise
awkward page turns and to make playing from it a real pleasure.
Particular care has been given to specifying acid-free, neutral-sized paper made from pulps
which have not been elemental chlorine bleached. This pulp is from farmed sustainable forests
and was produced with special regard for the environment.
Throughout, the printing and binding have been planned to ensure a sturdy, attractive publication
which should give years of enjoyment.
If your copy fails to meet our high standards, please inform us and we will gladly replace it.

Music Sales' complete catalogue describes thousands of titles and is available in full colour sections
by subject, direct from Music Sales Limited. Please state your areas of interest
and send a cheque/postal order for £1.50 for postage to:
Music Sales Limited, Newmarket Road, Bury St. Edmunds, Suffolk IP33 3YB.

www.musicsales.co.uk

Climb Ev'ry Mountain
(The Sound Of Music)

Words by Oscar Hammerstein II
Music by Richard Rodgers

Moderately

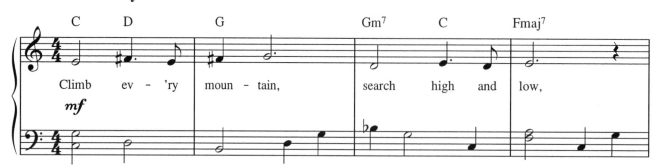

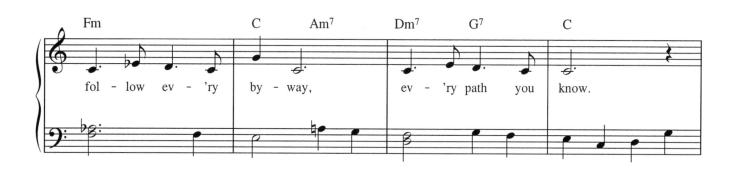

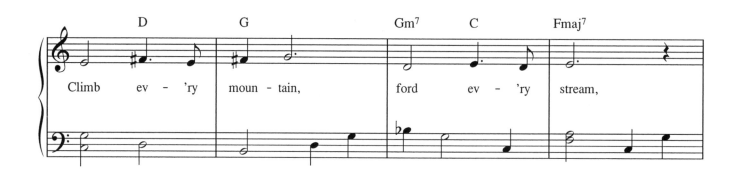

dream that will need_____ all the love you can give,_____ ev – 'ry

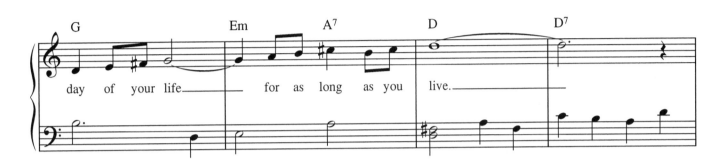

day of your life_____ for as long as you live._____

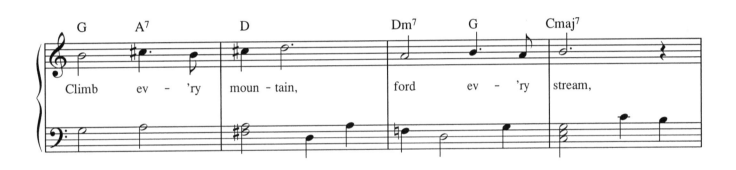

Climb ev – 'ry moun – tain, ford ev – 'ry stream,

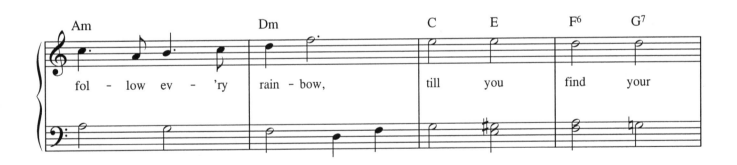

fol – low ev – 'ry rain – bow, till you find your

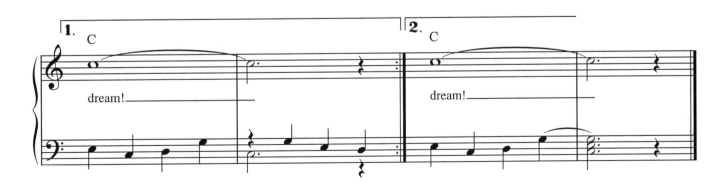

1. dream!_____

2. dream!_____

Consider Yourself

(Oliver!)

Words & Music by Lionel Bart

Moderately

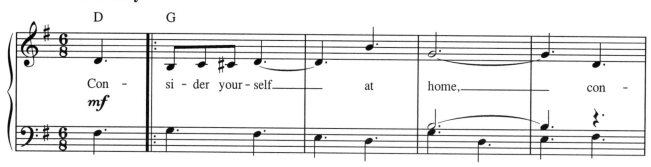

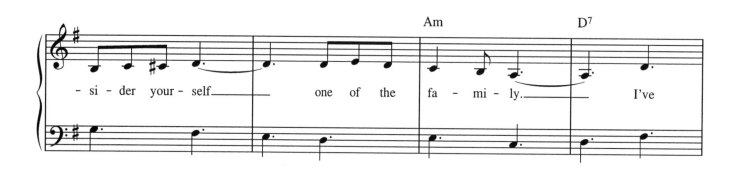

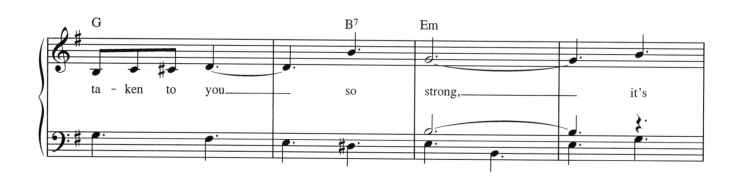

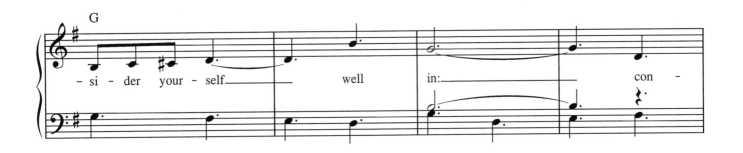

-si - der your - self___ well in:___ con -

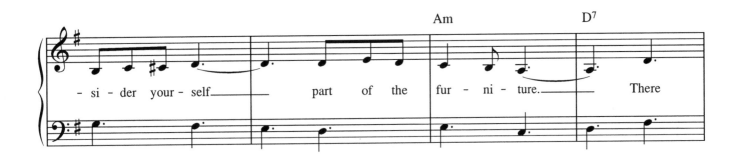

-si - der your - self___ part of the fur - ni - ture.___ There

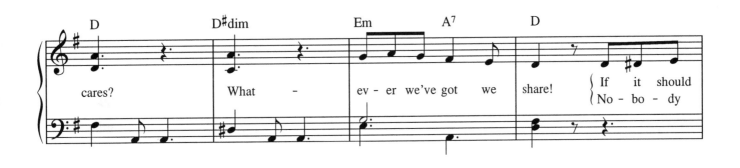

is - n't a lot___ to spare;___ who

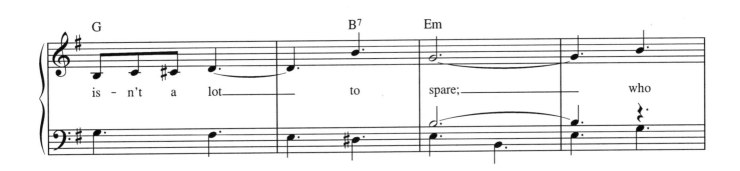

cares? What - ev - er we've got we share! If it should / No - bo - dy

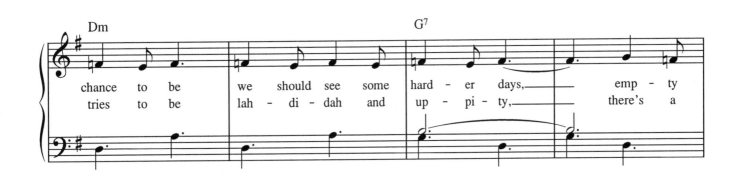

chance to be / tries to be we should see some / lah - di - dah and hard - er days,___ / up - pi - ty,___ emp - ty / there's a

7

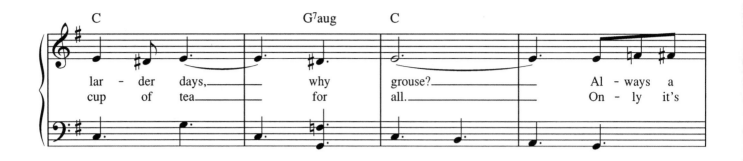

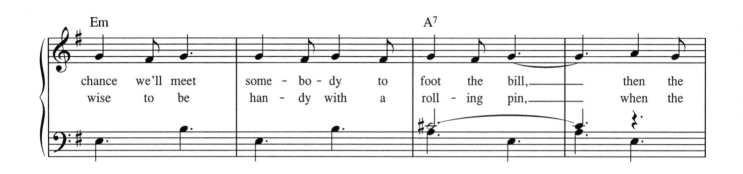

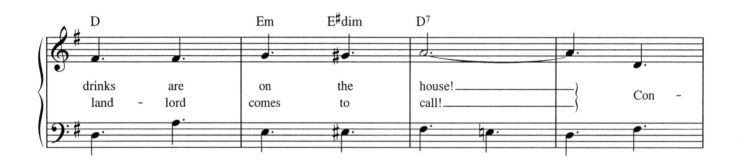

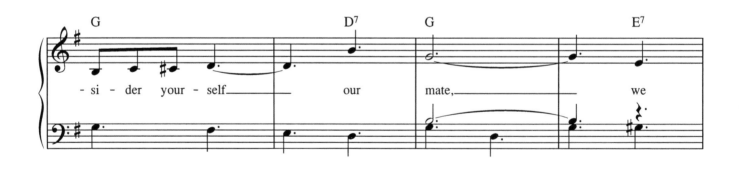

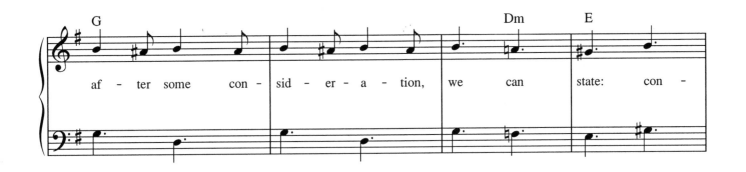

af - ter some con - sid - er - a - tion, we can state: con -

1. - si - der your - self____ one of us.____ Con -

2. - si - der your - self____ one of

us.____ *ff*

9

And All That Jazz

(Chicago)

Words by Fred Ebb
Music by John Kander

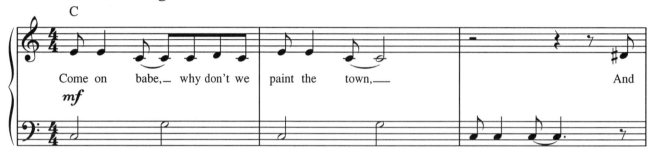

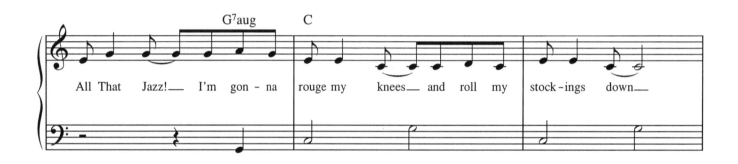

-ni-ted Drug___ in case we shake a - part___ and want a brand new start___ to

All That Jazz!___

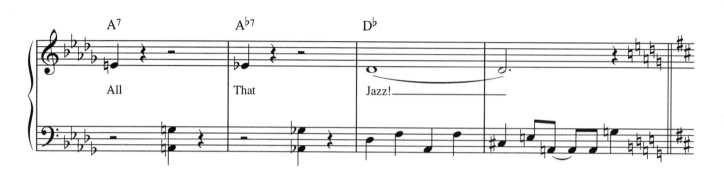

Oh,___ I'm gon - na see my She - ba shim - my shake.___ (And

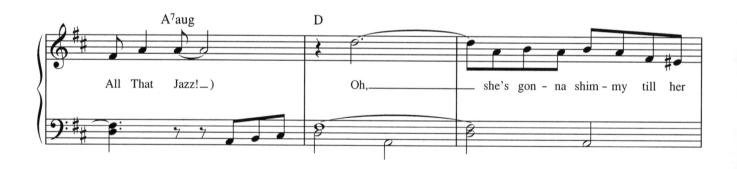

All That Jazz!___) Oh,___ she's gon - na shim - my till her

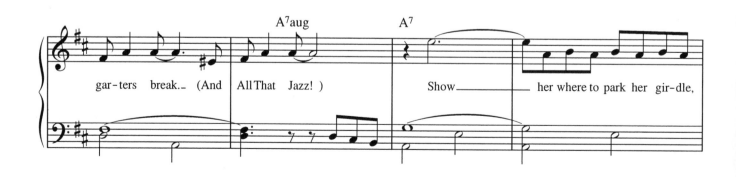

gar - ters break.___ (And All That Jazz!) Show___ her where to park her gir-dle,

Feeling Good
(The Roar Of The Greasepaint - The Smell Of The Crowd)
Words & Music by Leslie Bricusse & Anthony Newley

Moderately

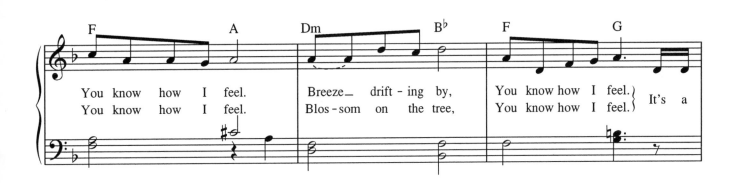

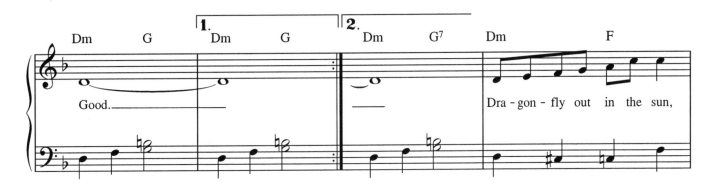

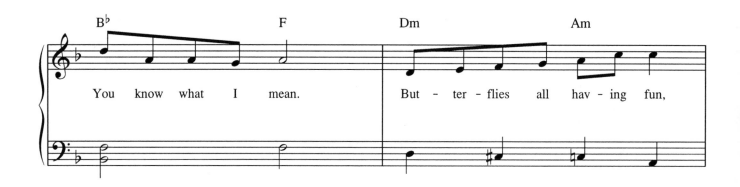

You know what I mean. But - ter - flies all hav - ing fun,

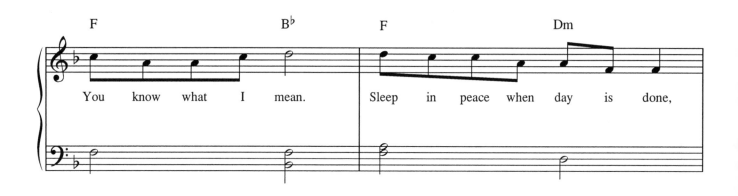

You know what I mean. Sleep in peace when day is done,

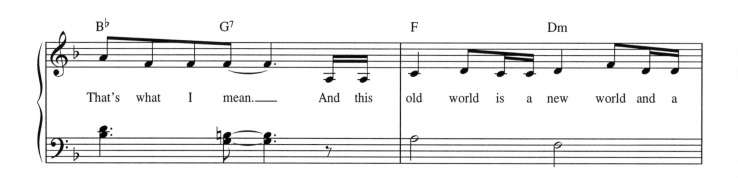

That's what I mean.___ And this old world is a new world and a

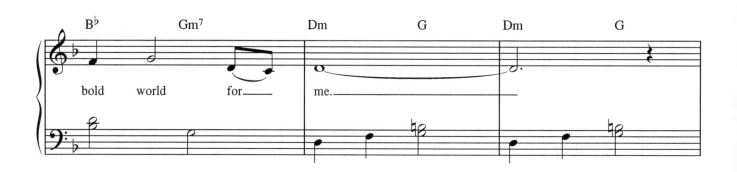

bold world for___ me.___

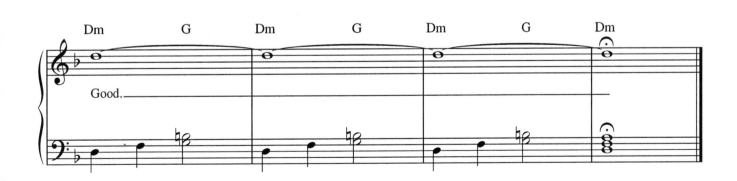

If My Friends Could See Me Now

(Sweet Charity)

Words by Dorothy Fields
Music by Cy Coleman

Strut tempo

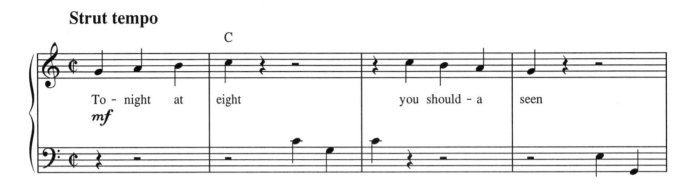

To - night at eight you should - a seen

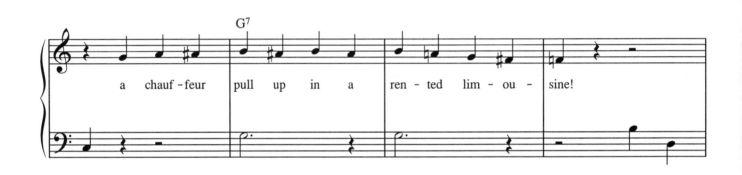

a chauf -feur pull up in a ren - ted lim - ou - sine!

My neigh-bours burned! They like to die! When I

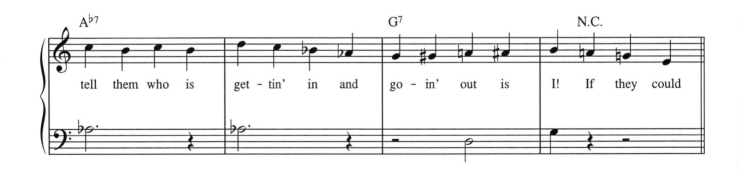

tell them who is get - tin' in and go - in' out is I! If they could

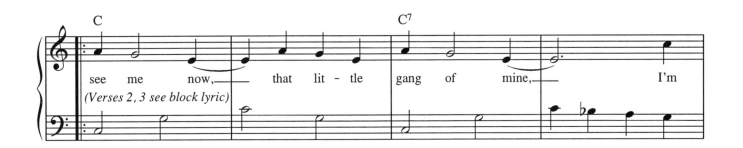

see me now,___ that lit - tle gang of mine,___ I'm
(Verses 2, 3 see block lyric)

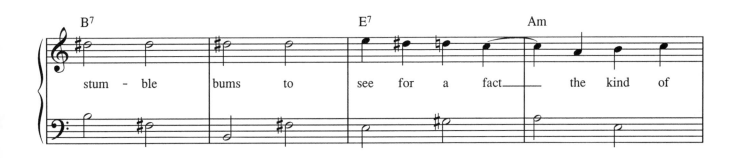

eat - ing fan - cy chow and drink - ing fan - cy wine.___ I'd like those

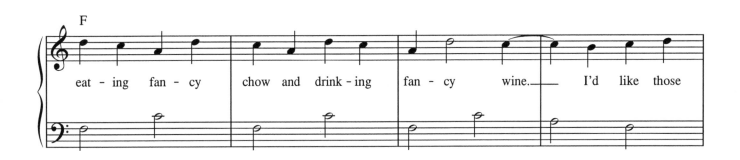

stum - ble bums to see for a fact___ the kind of

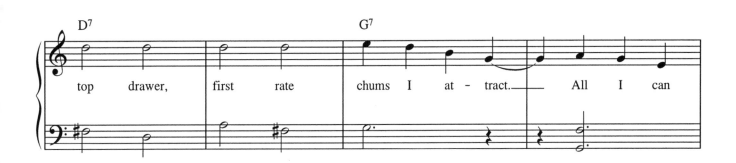

top drawer, first rate chums I at - tract.___ All I can

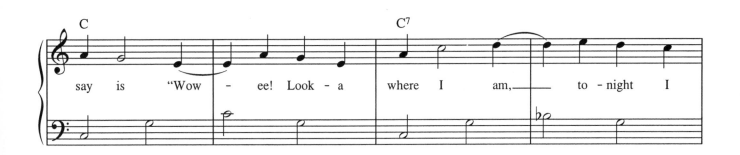

say is "Wow - ee! Look - a where I am,___ to - night I

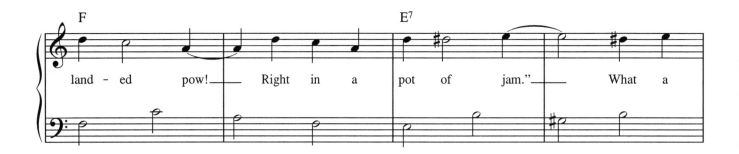

land - ed pow!— Right in a pot of jam."— What a

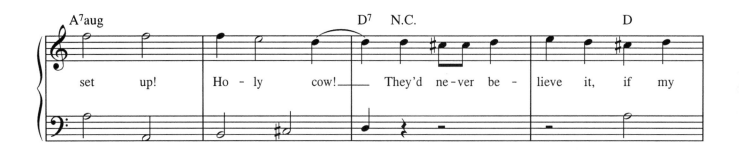

set up! Ho - ly cow!— They'd ne-ver be - lieve it, if my

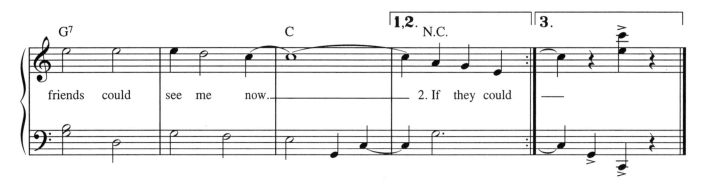

friends could see me now.———————— 2. If they could

Verse 2:

If they could see me now, my little dusty group,
Traipsin' round this million dollar chicken coop.
I'd hear those thrift shop cats say, "Brother, get her!
Draped on a bedspread made from three kinds of fur."
All I can say is "Wow! Wait till the riff and raff
See just exactly how he signed this autograph."
What a build up! Holy cow! They'd never believe it,
If my friends could see me now.

Verse 3:

If they could see me now, alone with Mister V.
Who's waitin' on me like he was a maitre 'd.
I hear my buddies saying, "Crazy, what gives?
Tonight she's living like the other half lives."
To think the highest brow which I must say is he
Should pick the lowest brow which there is no doubt is me.
What a step up! Holy cow! They'd never believe it,
If my friends could see me now.

June Is Bustin' Out All Over

(Carousel)

Music by Richard Rodgers
Words by Oscar Hammerstein II

Moderately

1. June is bust-in' out all o - ver!___ All

(Verses 2 & 3 see block lyric)

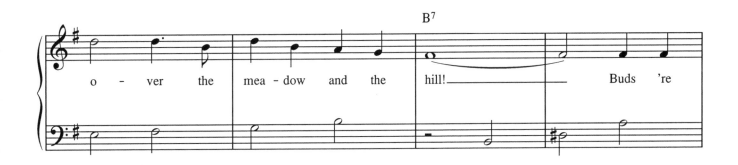

o - ver the mea-dow and the hill!___ Buds 're

bust-in' out a bush-es And the romp-in' riv - er push - es Ev - 'ry

lit - tle wheel that wheels be - side a mill!___

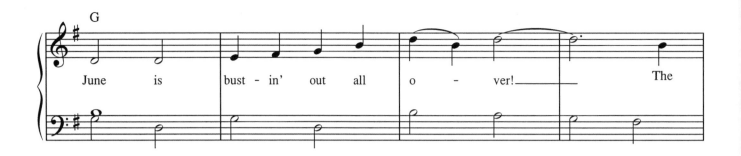

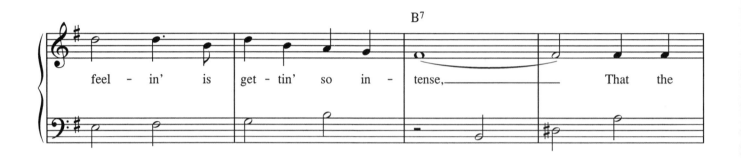

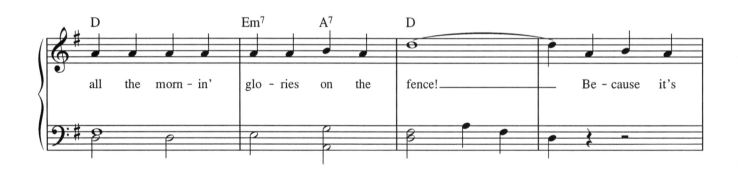

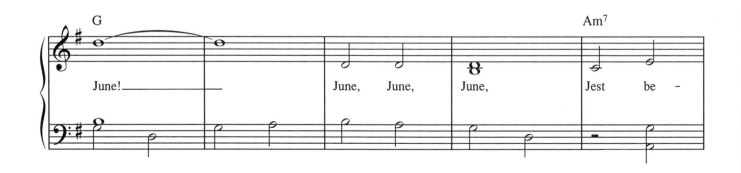

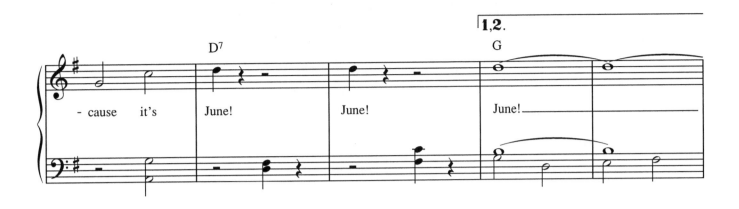

- cause   it's   June!   June!   June!

June!

Verse 2:

June is bustin' out all over!
The saplin's are bustin' out with sap!
Love has found my brother, junior,
And my sister's even lunier!
And my ma is gettin' kittenish with pap!
June is bustin' out all over!
To ladies the men are payin' court.
Lots-a ships are kept at anchor
Jest because the captains hanker
Fer a comfort they can only get in port!
Because it's June! June, June June,
Jest because it's June! June! June!

Verse 3:

June is bustin' out all over!
The ocean is full of Jacks and Jills.
With her little tail a-swishin'
Ev'ry lady fish is wishin'
That a male would come and grab her by the gills!
June is bust-in' out all over!
The sheep aren't sleepin' anymore!
All the rams that chase the ewe sheep
Are determined there'll be new sheep
And the ewe sheep aren't even keepin' score!
On account it's June! June, June, June,
Jest because it's June! June! June!

Master Of The House

(Les Misérables)

Words by Herbert Kretzmer
Music by Claude-Michel Schönberg
Original Text by Alain Boublil & Jean-Marc Natel

Moderately

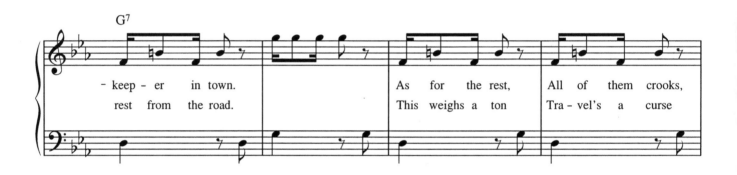

- tent Who's con - tent to be
- looked Till I'm sa - tis - fied...

Ma - ster of the House
Food be - yond com - pare

Do - ling out the charm Rea - dy with a hand - shake And an o - pen palm.
Food be - yond be - lief Mix it in a min - cer And pre - tend it's beef.

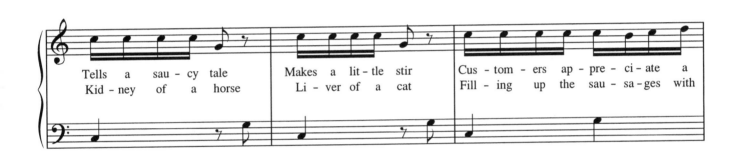

Tells a sau - cy tale Makes a lit - tle stir Cus - tom - ers ap - pre - ci - ate a
Kid - ney of a horse Li - ver of a cat Fill - ing up the sau - sa - ges with

bon vi - veur! Glad to do my friends a fa - vour Does-n't cost me to be
this and that! Re - si - dents are more than wel - come Bri - dal suite is oc - cu -pied!

nice But no - thing gets you no - thing Ev - 'ry - thing has got a lit - tle
Rea - son - a - ble char - ges Plus some lit - tle ex - tra on the

25

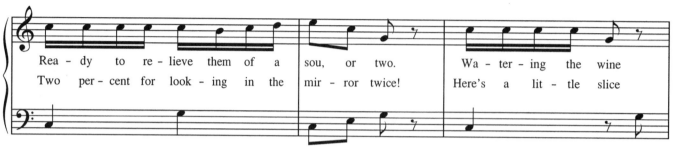

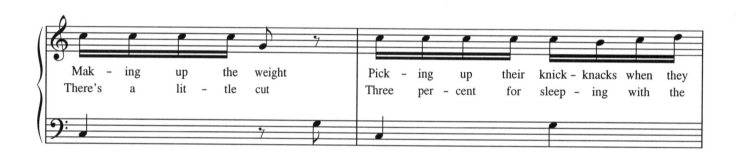

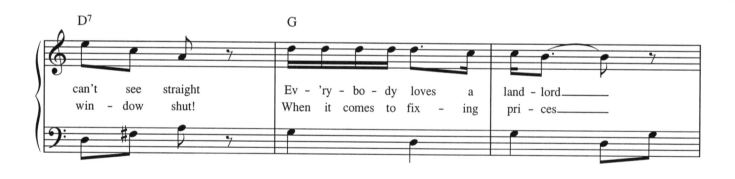

Me And My Girl

(Me And My Girl)

Music by Noel Gay
Words by Douglas Furber & Arthur Rose

Moderately

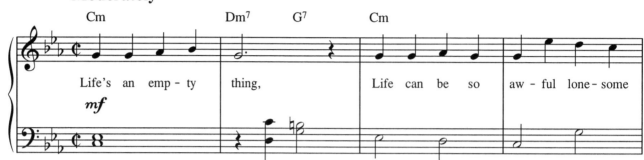

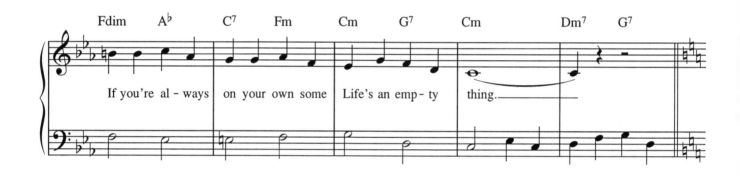

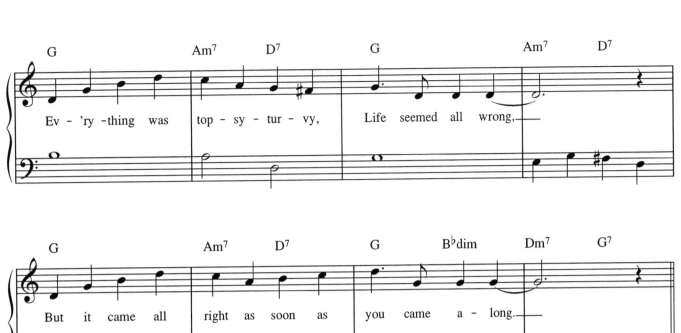

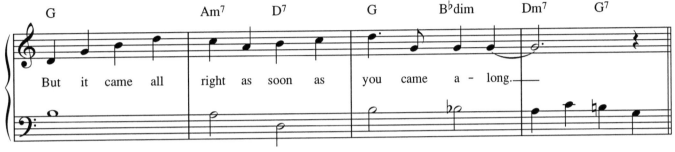

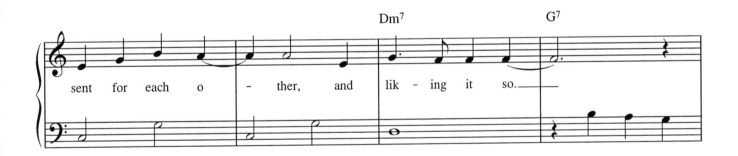

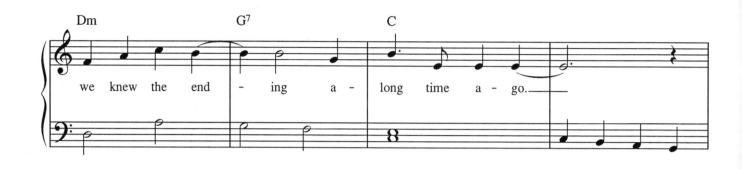

we knew the end - ing a - long time a - go.

Some lit - tle church with a big stee - ple,

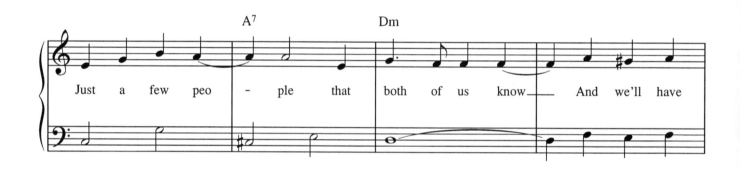

Just a few peo - ple that both of us know And we'll have

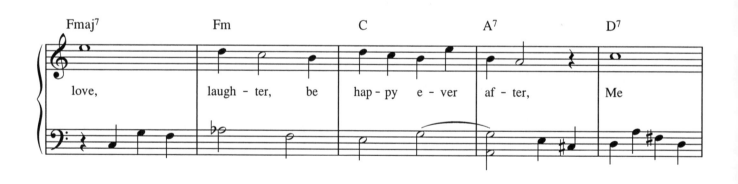

love, laugh - ter, be hap - py e - ver af - ter, Me

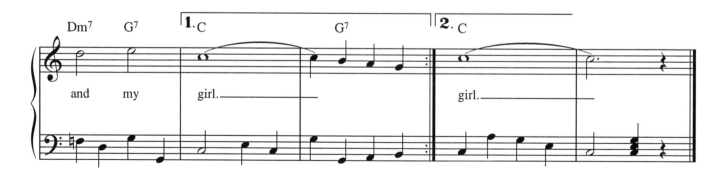

and my girl. girl.

Memory

(Cats)

Music by Andrew Lloyd Webber
Text by Trevor Nunn after T.S. Eliot

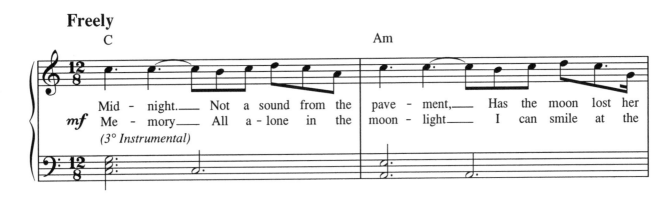

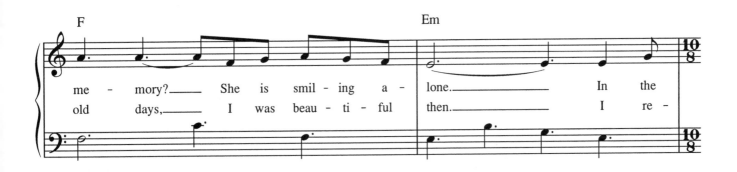

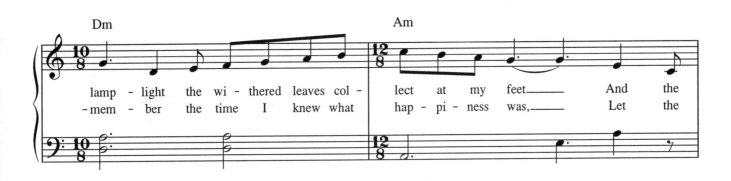

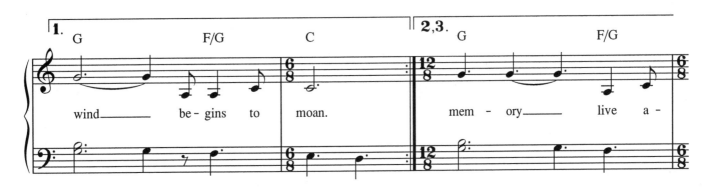

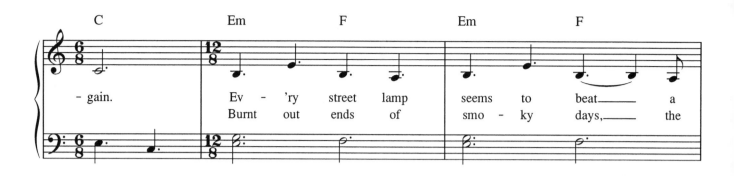

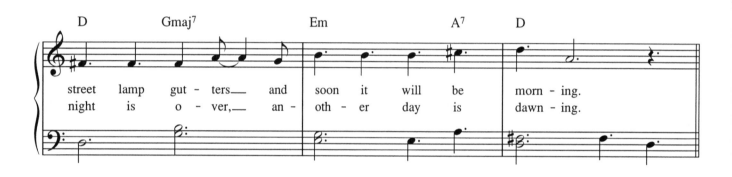

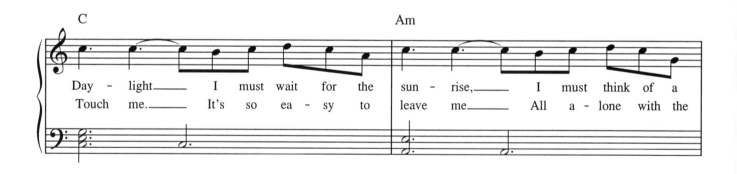

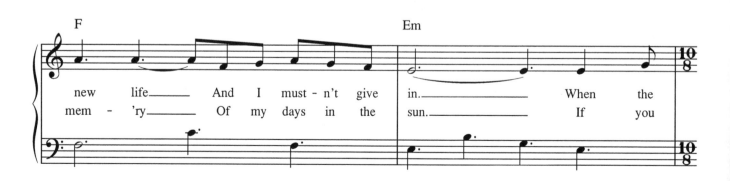

32

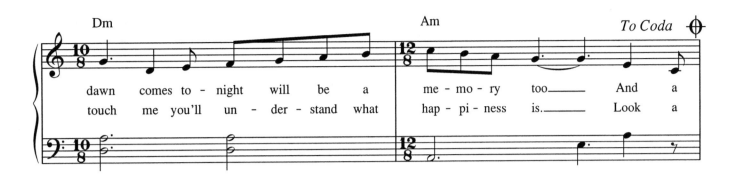

dawn comes to - night will be a me - mo - ry too_____ And a
touch me you'll un - der - stand what hap - pi - ness is._____ Look a

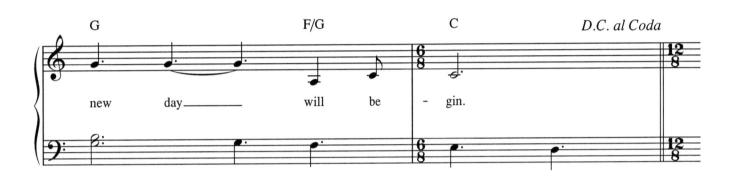

new day_____ will be - gin.

CODA

new day_____ has be - gun.

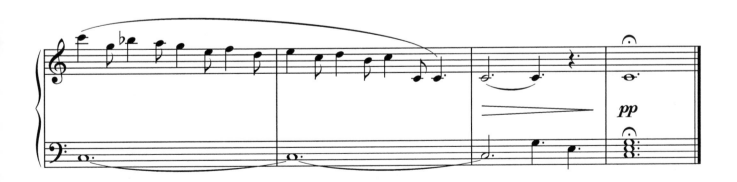

pp

Superstar

(Jesus Christ Superstar)

Music by Andrew Lloyd Webber
Lyrics by Tim Rice

Lively rock

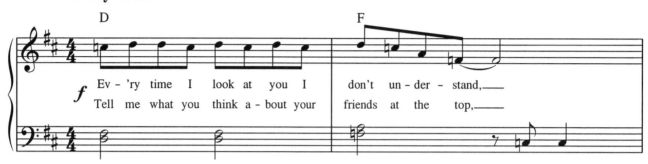

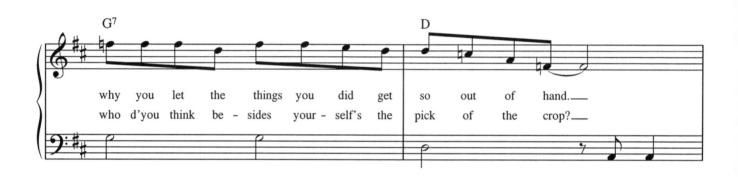

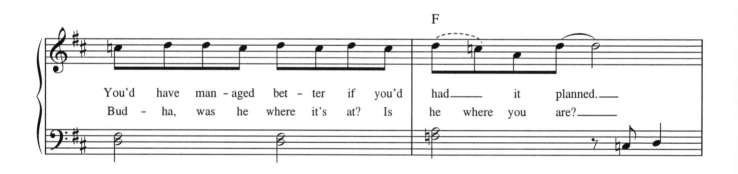

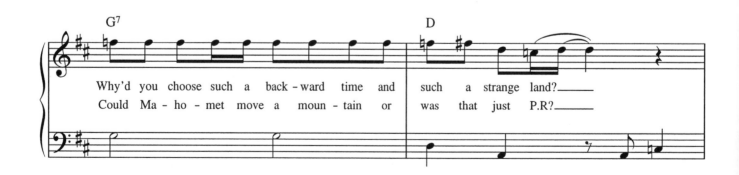

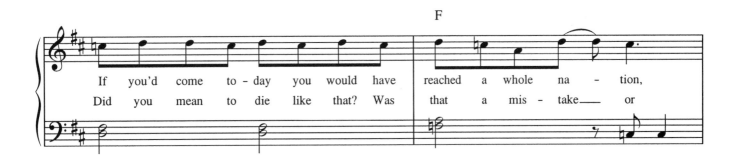

If you'd come to-day you would have reached a whole na - tion,
Did you mean to die like that? Was that a mis - take___ or

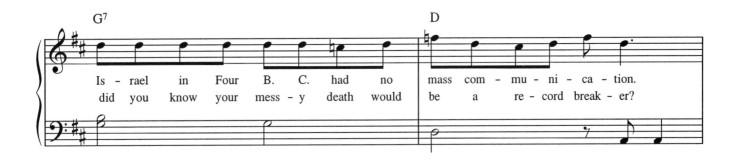

Is - rael in Four B. C. had no mass com - mu - ni - ca - tion.
did you know your mess - y death would be a re - cord break - er?

Don't you get me wrong,___ Don't you get me wrong,___ Don't you get me wrong,___

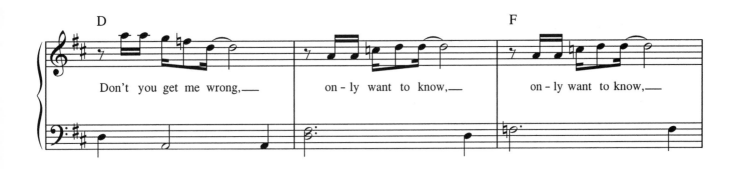

Don't you get me wrong,___ on - ly want to know,___ on - ly want to know,___

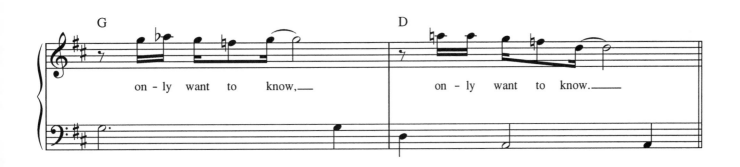

on - ly want to know,___ on - ly want to know.___

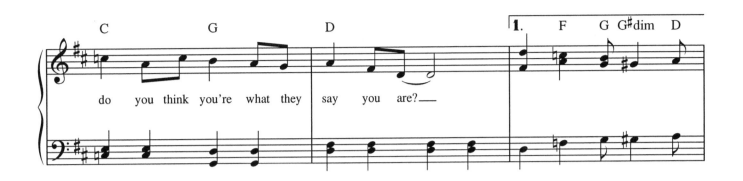

do you think you're what they say you are? ___

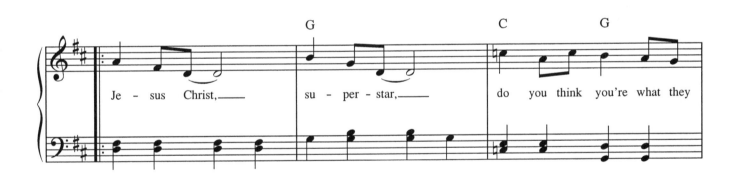

Je - sus Christ, ___ su - per - star, ___ do you think you're what they

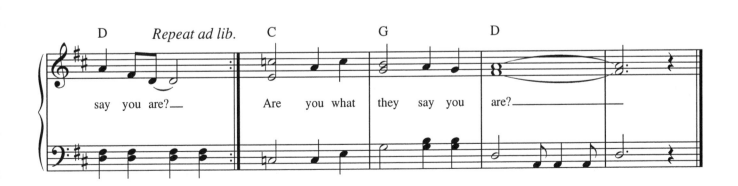

say you are? ___ Are you what they say you are? ___

Some Enchanted Evening

(South Pacific)

Words by Oscar Hammerstein II
Music by Richard Rodgers

Moderately slow

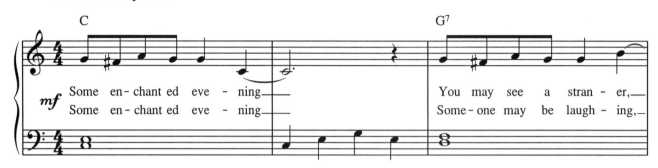

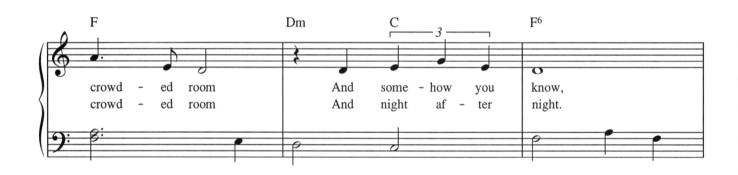

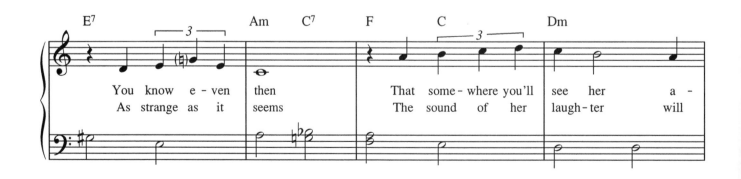

side

And make her your own,

Or all through your

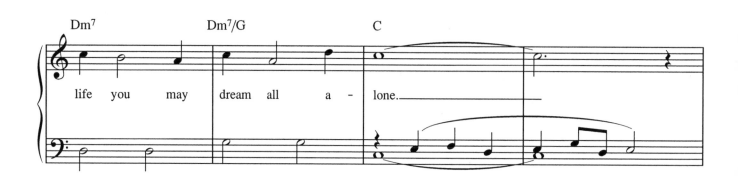

life you may dream all a - lone.

Once you have found her,

Ne-ver let her go.

Once you have found her,

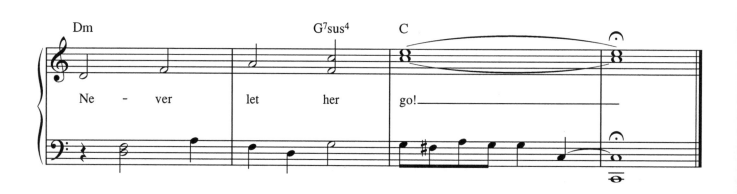

Ne - ver let her go!

What I Did For Love

(A Chorus Line)

Words by Edward Kleban
Music by Marvin Hamlisch

Moderately

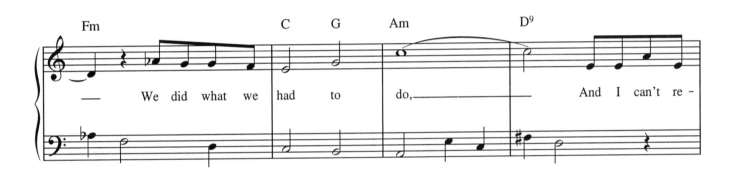

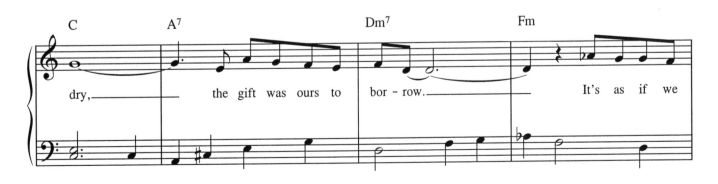

al - ways knew,_____ But I won't for - get What I did for

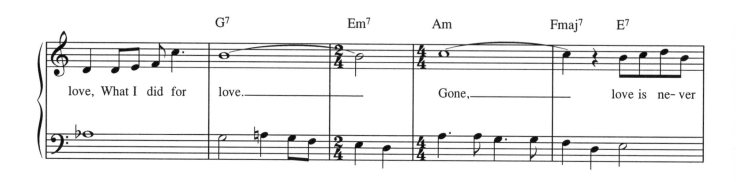

love, What I did for love._____ Gone,_____ love is ne- ver

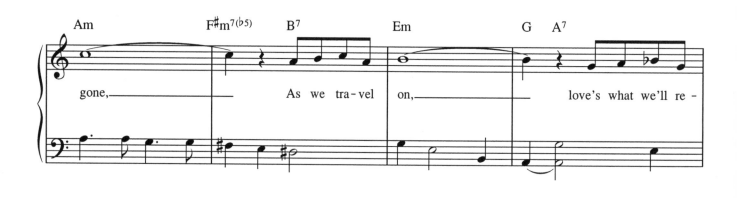

gone,_____ As we tra-vel on,_____ love's what we'll re-

- mem - ber._____ Kiss to-day_ good - bye,_____ and point me t'ward to-

Dm⁷ ... Fm ... C ... G

- mor - row._____ Wish me luck, the same to

Am⁷ ... D⁹ ... F ... C ... Dm⁷ ... G⁷

you._____ Won't for - get, can't re - gret What I did for

C ... Dm ... G⁷ ... C ... Dm ... G⁷

love, What I did for love, What I did for

1. C ... N.C. ... **2.** C

love._____ Kiss to - day__ good - love._____

You'll Never Walk Alone

(Carousel)

Music by Richard Rodgers
Words by Oscar Hammerstein II

With warmth, like a hymn

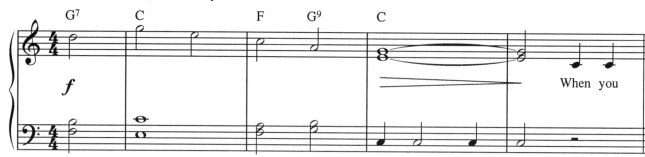

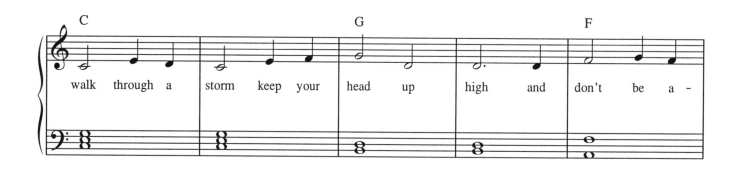

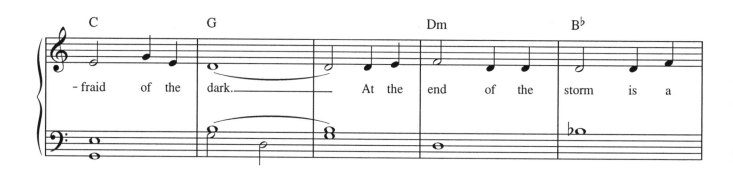

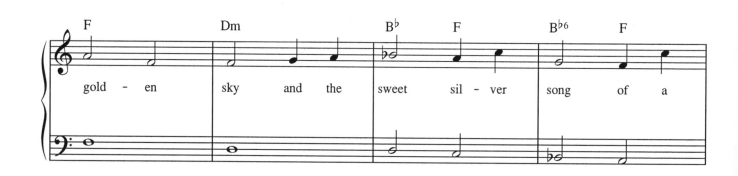

lark.___ Walk on through the wind, walk on through the

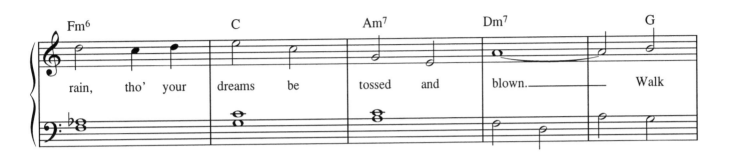

rain, tho' your dreams be tossed and blown.___ Walk

on, walk on, with hope in your heart, and you'll nev - er

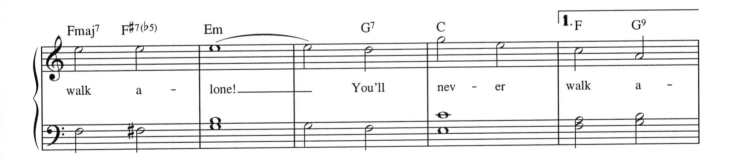

walk a - lone!___ You'll nev - er walk a -

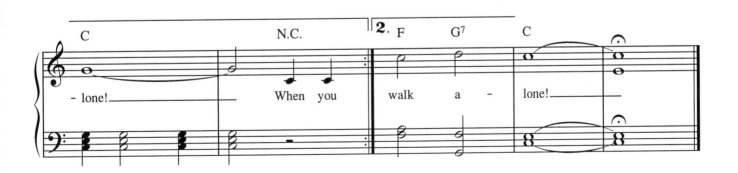

- lone!___ When you walk a - lone!___

You're The One That I Want

(Grease)

Words & Music by John Farrar

Moderately

I got chills.
filled

They're mul - ti - ply - in'.
with af - fec - tion

And I'm lo - sin' con - trol.
you're too shy to con - vey,

'Cause the
Me - di -

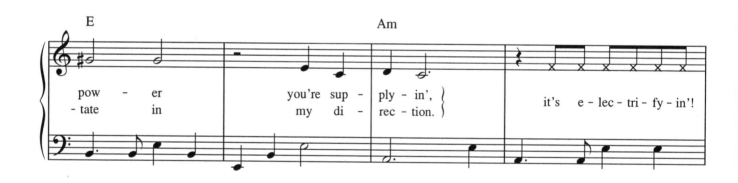

pow - er
- tate in

you're sup - ply - in',
my di - rec - tion.

it's e - lec - tri - fy - in'!

Feel your way.

I bet - ter shape
You bet - ter shape

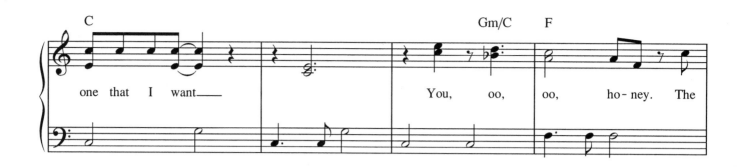

one that I want___ You, oo, oo, ho-ney. The

one that I want___ You, oo, oo, ho-ney. The

one that I want_____ You, oo,

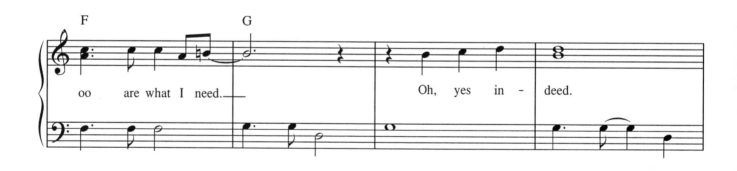

oo are what I need.___ Oh, yes in - deed.

If you're You're the one that I want!___